The bug, the boy, and the bear
want to paint a picture.

The bear has a big brush.
He paints something big.

The boy's brush is not
as big as the bear's.
He paints
something smaller.

The bug has a tiny brush.
He paints something smaller.

They paint for a long time.

The bear hangs the
picture on the wall.

Then the bug, the bear,
and the boy sit down
to look at it.

They are pleased.